THE TREA
BY HO

ALTHOUGH HOMOEOPATHY HAS been described as 'the most complete and scientific system of healing the world has ever seen', the veterinary aspect has received scant attention, but the remedies are just as effective in animals as they are in humans.

A VERY EXPERIENCED practitioner has written this book. In it Mr Sheppard indicates proven homoeopathic remedies for common ailments to which dogs are prone. The medicines recommended are those most likely to overcome the diseases named: they are simple to administer and do not produce any side-effects.

By the same author
THE TREATMENT OF CATS
BY HOMOEOPATHY

THE TREATMENT
OF DOGS
BY HOMOEOPATHY

by

K. SHEPPARD

Illustrated by
Steven Brown

THE C. W. DANIEL COMPANY LTD.,
1 Church Path, Saffron Walden, Essex, England.

First published 1963
Second edition (completely revised and reset)
April 1972
Reprinted July 1976
Illustrated edition 1981
Reprinted 1983
Reprinted 1986

ISBN 0 85032 079 8
Printed in Great Britain by
Hillman Printers (Frome) Ltd., Somerset.

INTRODUCTION

I have been asked to write this book as a companion to my book on Cats.

Despite the fact that Homoeopathy was founded by Christian Frederic Samuel Hahnemann in the year 1796 and has spread throughout the world, it still meets with opposition from those who condemn it prior to investigation.

The word 'Homoeopathy' is derived from the Greek: homoios, 'similar', and pathos, 'state' or 'condition', and is the term for that school which treats disease by the 'Similia Similibus Curentur' theory, i.e., 'Like Cures Like'.

These three principles are the main characteristics of the Homoeopathic schools:—

1.   The effect of drugs is tested on the healthy human body.

2.   Application of the principle 'Similia Similibus Curentur' (Let likes be cured by likes) in such diseases as can be healed by internal remedies.

3.   Dispensing the remedy in such small doses that it can have no injurious effects.

From the humane point of view alone the advantages of testing the efficacy of drugs on the healthy human body instead of experimenting upon animals, who cannot express their feelings, and may not react in the same way, is very great.

It is well known that Sulphur causes and cures rashes; that Ipecacuanha causes and cures sickness and vomiting. These are some illustrations of the truth of the Homoeopathic principle.

The explanation of this twofold effect is to be found in the dispensing of the drug — large doses have the contrary effect of small ones. Thus, for example, Rhubarb in large doses is used as an aperient, while a Homoeopathic dose will cure the form of diarrhoea for which it is the identical remedy. Likewise, Opium in large doses stupefies, and causes constipation, whereas in Homoeopathic doses it stimulates, and will also cure constipation, so that large doses are frequently injurious whereas small · doses are beneficial. When that is proved to be so in healthy bodies, it is much more so when applied to diseased body.

It is therefore obvious that Homoeopathy is a method built up on scientific foundations, perhaps one of the greatest advantages is that the minute doses prescribed can have no injurious secondary effects, so that drug poisoning (not infrequently the result of strong Allopathic medicines) need never arise in Homoeopathic treatment. The medicines are pleasant to take, they can be safely given to the smallest puppy without distressing the animal and no injections are necessary.

A further advantage is that Homoeopathic remedies can be applied at once, even when a disease cannot be clearly diagnosed. By knowing the effect of a drug on a healthy body, having carefully observed the distressing symptoms, one can give the indicated remedy at once, and thus one can often succeed in arresting the disease.

A further advantage is that one can do something to give relief where a veterinary surgeon is not available, as by administering Arnica for shock in cases of injuries.

Since in Homoeopathy one treats the individual and not a named disease, it is not possible, in a book of this kind, to give more than an indication of the remedies with the symptoms that would call for them. In an outbreak of Distemper many dogs might be affected differently and each would require a different remedy according to its symptoms, so that one must learn to be observant.

The remedy should be applied following the Hahnemann laws:—

(1) The single remedy.
(2) The minute dose.
(3) Given on the totality of the symptoms found in the individual patient.

Homoeopathy acts very quickly *if one gets the*

right remedy. The lower potencies such as 3 to 6, do not have as rapid or as far-reaching effects as the higher potencies, so it is safer for anyone inexperienced in Homoeopathy to use the lower potencies — do not be in a hurry to repeat the dose. They should be discontinued 24 hours after the symptoms are relieved.

The potency is indicated by the number appearing after the name of the remedy.

The remedies should be stored in a cool, dry and preferably dark place, and kept apart from all strong smelling lotions, as these will destroy their efficacy.

Remedies can be obtained already prepared in the potency required, in various forms such as powder, granules, pilules, liquids, tablets, from any homoeopathic chemist.

HOMOEOPATHIC REMEDIES
AND ABBREVIATIONS

Aconitum Napellus	*Aconite*
AEthiops Antimonialis	*AEthiops*
Alfalfa	*Alfalfa*
Antimonium Tartaricum	*Ant Tart*
Apis Mellifica	*Apis*
Apocynum Cannabinum	*Apocynum Can*
Arnica Montana	*Arnica*
Arsenicum Album	*Arsenicum*
Bacillinum	*Bacillinum*
Baptisia Tinctoria	*Baptisia*
Belladonna	*Belladonna*
Bellis Perennis	*Bellis Per*
Bryonia Alba	*Bryonia*
Cactus Grandiflorus	*Cactus*
Calcarea Carbonica	*Calc Carb*
Calcarea Fluorata	*Calc Fluor*
Calcarea Phosphorica	*Calc Phos*
Calcareum	*Calcareum*
Calendula Officinalis	*Calendula*
Camphora	*Camphor*
Cantharis Vesicator	*Cantharis*
Capsicum Annuum	*Capsicum*
Carbo Vegetabilis and Nux Vomica (combined)	*Carbo-Nux*
Carcinosinum	*Carcinosinum*

Causticum	*Causticum*
Chamomilla	*Chamomilla*
Chelidonium Majus	*Chelidonium*
Chenopodium Anthelminticum	*Chenopodium*
Chichona Officinalis	*China*
Cimicifuga Racemosa	*Cimicifuga*
Cina	*Cina*
Colchicum Autumnale	*Colchicum*
Colocynthis	*Colocynth*
Crataegus Oxyacantha	*Crataegus*
Crotalus Horridus	*Crotalus Horr*
Cuprum Metallicum	*Cuprum*
Dioscorea Villosa	*Dioscorea*
Distemperinum	*Distemperinum*
Euphorbia Corollata	*Euphorbia Cor*
Euphrasia Officinalis	*Euphrasia*
Ferrum Phosphoricum	*Ferrum Phos*
Ferrum Picricum	*Ferrum Pic*
Filix Mas	*Filix Mas*
Gelsemium Sempervirens	*Gelsemium*
Glonoinum	*Glonine*
Graphites	*Graphites*
Hamamelis	*Hamamelis*
Hecla Lava	*Hecla Lava*
Hepar Sulphuris Calcareum	*Hepar Sulph*
Hyoscyamus Niger	*Hyoscyamus*
Hypericum Perforatum	*Hypericum*
Ignatia Amara	*Ignatia*
Iodine	*Iodine*
Ipecacuanha	*Ipecacuanha*

Kali Muriaticum	*Kali Mur*
Kali Phosphoricum	*Kali Phos*
Ledum Palustre	*Ledum*
Lycopodium Clavatum	*Lycopodium*
Magnesia Phosphorica	*Mag Phos*
Mercurius Corrosivus	*Merc Cor*
Mercurius Solubilis Hahnemanni	*Merc Sol*
Natrum Muriaticum	*Nat Mur*
Natrum Phosphoricum	*Nat Phos*
Natrum Sulphuricum	*Nat Sulph*
Nux Vomica	*Nux Vom*
Opium	*Opium*
Phosphoricum Acidum	*Phos Acid*
Phosphorus	*Phosphorus*
Phytolacca Decandra	*Phytolacca*
Podophyllum Peltatum	*Podophyllum*
Psoricum	*Psorinum*
Pulsatilla Nigricans	*Pulsatilla*
Pyrogenium	*Pyrogen*
Rhododendron Chrysanthum	*Rhododendron*
Rhus Toxicodendron	*Rhus Tox*
Ruta Graveolens	*Ruta*
Scirrhinum	*Scirrhinum*
Sepia Officinalis	*Sepia*
Silicea Terra	*Silica*
Spigelia Anthelmia	*Spigelia*
Spongia Tosta	*Spongia*
Sulphur	*Sulphur*
Symphytum Officinale	*Symphytum*
Tarentula Cubensis	*Tarentula Cub*

Tellurium	*Tellurium*
Terebinthina	*Terebinthina*
Thlaspi Bursa Pastoris	*Thlaspi Bur*
Thuja Occidentalis	*Thuja*
Tuberculinum	*Tuberculinum*
Uranium Nitricum	*Uranium Nit*
Urtica Urens	*Urtica Urens*
Zincum Metallicum	*Zincum Met*

IMPORTANT NOTES: All remedies to be given internally unless otherwise stated.

Where **CARBO-NUX** is recommended it is a combination of **CARBO VEG 6** and **NUX VOMICA 6**. This can be supplied by a Homoeopathic Chemist.

The sign ϕ indicates Mother Tincture.

ABRASIONS
Symptoms: The skin is damaged or rubbed off, leaving a raw surface.

Bathe with *Calendula Lotion,* made by adding one part of *Calendula* ϕ to ten parts of water.

Internally, give *Arnica* 6, two-hourly (or in the 30th potency four-hourly).

Should the nerves be bruised, give *Hypericum* in the same way instead of *Arnica.*

ABSCESSES
Symptoms: Swellings, with the formation of pus, accompanied by fever and pain.

Give *Tarentula Cub.* 30, three times a day.

Externally, bathe with *Calendula Lotion* (made by adding a teaspoonful of *Calendula* ϕ to half a cup of warm water). When the abscess be broken and the bulk of the discharge has come away, apply *Calendula Ointment* instead of the lotion.

Tarentula Cub. sometimes aborts the abscess without further trouble.

ALBUMINARIA

Symptoms: Unusual thirst, loss of condition, even though eating well. Coat starey; the dog passes water more frequently than usual and misbehaves in the house at night. There are various causes but it may develop after severe exercise such as letting a dog run after a bicycle, which should never be allowed.

The diet is important. Feed on boiled white fish or rabbit, and rusked brown bread. Avoid indigestible foods and fats.

Give *Calc Phos 3x and Kali Mur-3x,* three times daily each, the first remedy before and the second after meals supplemented by a dose of *Kali Phos.* 30 for the nervous condition and *Nat Phos.* 30 as this may be due to over acidity; each of these two last named remedies to be given once a week, 3 or 4 days apart, dogs respond excellently to these remedies which supply the affected cells with the inorganic salts which they lack and restore the tissues to a healthy normal condition.

ANAEMIA

Symptoms: Mouth and lids of eyes pale. Sometimes loss of condition, thirst, constipation; the dog appears languid and disinclined for exercise. Anaemia may be merely a symptom of some much more serious trouble, and the dog should be thoroughly overhauled by a competent vet, to make sure there is no such trouble to account for the condition.

In fat flabby dogs, give *Calc Phos* 3, eight-hourly.

In thin, puny dogs, which have had, or show signs of Rickets, give *Silica* 6, eight-hourly. If the dog also has constipation give *Nat Mur* 6, six-hourly.
Food is very important. The dog should have plenty of meat, goat's milk, eggs, and free exercise in the fresh air.

AMAUROSIS
Symptoms: A disease of the eyes, often with total loss of sight due to a paralysis of the nerves of the eye, sometimes a sequel to Distemper.

Seldom curable.

The eyes are clear, with the pupils very dilated and they do not contract to light.

Try the following remedies for a week at a time; if no improvement, try the next: (1) *Gelsemium* 3, four-hourly; (2) *Belladonna* 3, four-hourly; (3) *Nux Vom* 3, two-hourly; (4) *Phosphorus* 3, two-hourly.

ANAL GLANDS
Dogs frequently get congestion and irritation of these glands.

Symptoms: The dog drags itself along the ground (this is usually attributed to worms). It frequently licks the anus and may suddenly look round and tuck in the tail as if it were pricked. There is a swelling on one or each side of the anus and sometimes an abscess forms there.

If the anus is red and the dog generally in poor condition, give *Sulphur* 30 every two or three days for a week or more.

If the dog should be constipated, give *Carbo-Nux* 6 three times a day after meals.

If the condition has become chronic and an abscess has formed, then give *Silica* 30 every two days at first and later less frequently.

If there is great sensitiveness to the slightest touch, give *Hepar Sulph* 30 instead of *Silica*, every two days at first and later less frequently.

Externally, bathe the parts with *Calendula Lotion* (made by adding one part of *Calendula* φ to ten parts of water).

ANUS, PROLAPSE OF
This sometimes occurs in young puppies; it may also occur in older dogs. It is usually caused by straining with diarrhoea; it is also a sign of constitutional weakness.

Symptoms: The lower bowel protrudes from the body and if it is not speedily relieved becomes inflamed and swollen and the animal keeps straining.

Return the protruding part as quickly as possible after applying *Calendula Ointment* to the part (it is best to hold the dog up by the hind legs and to keep in this position for a little while in order to do this). Firm pressure with the fingers is required to return the prolapsed part; when this has been accomplished apply a cold *Calendula Lotion Compress*, made by adding one part of *Calendula Ø* to ten parts of water, to the part.

The difficulty is to keep the part in. Recurrence in puppies may sometimes be prevented by the use of (1) *Calc Carb 6x* morning and evening. (2) *Ruta 1x* every eight hours might help if the prolapse occurs at every motion. (3) *Podophyllum* 6 three times a day, should there be diarrhoea, especially during teething.

If, however, the prolapse keeps recurring, an operation may be necessary.

APOPLEXY

Symptoms: This is sometimes met with in old dogs. There may be convulsions, the dog suddenly falls down and there is loss of consciousness. The eyes are congested and the tongue a dark colour.

The seizure may last for some time. Upon recovery the dog may show symptoms of paralysis of more or less severity.

Keep the dog absolutely quiet and in a darkened room while in the stroke.

Give *Belladonna* 3 every 15 minutes while the dog is showing signs of acute congestion. The remedy may be placed on the tongue or inside the lips.

If the dog is known to be constipated, give *Opium* 3 every 15 minutes instead of *Belladonna* until it recovers consciousness.

When it recovers consciousness give *Arnica* 3 hourly for several doses and later three times a day.

The diet should be very light, liquids, milk, bread and milk, or soups.

Should paralysis follow, see under that heading.

APPETITE, WANT OF

Some dogs are delicate and natural bad doers; these are often of dainty appetite and difficult as to diet.

Try a change of food. Some such dogs will eat either raw or cooked meat or fish, and show preference for one or the other — stewed rabbit or liver will often tempt them.

A course of *Carbo-Nux* 6 given twice a day after meals, combined with plenty of free exercise in the fresh air, will often tone up the digestive organs and help to overcome this fussiness.

Rhus Tox 3 six-hourly is of great value when there is a complete loss of appetite without any apparent cause.

Nat Phos 3x three times a day if due to acidity.

APPETITE, DEPRAVED
Symptoms: Puppies, and sometimes adult dogs, will pick up and eat filth of all kinds, stones, coal and excreta.

It is important to see that the animal is free from worms as these parasites are sometimes the cause of this unpleasant habit. It may also be due to indigestion. It is not infrequently simply a bad habit picked up from another dog.

If worms are suspected the condition should be treated (see Worms).

The puppy or dog should be sternly reprimanded when it picks up bones or other food in the street; it will quickly learn not to do so if it be corrected each time.

A course of *Calc Carb* 6 morning and evening for a week or so often helps these cases, which may be due to a calcium deficiency, or *Carbo-Nux* 6 after meals if due to a weak digestion.

ASTHMA
Symptoms: Difficult or spasmodic breathing usually accompanied by a troublesome cough and often vomiting of saliva like whipped white of egg.

The dog does not appear to be ill and the attacks may be infrequent, but are distressing when they occur.

This is usually an affection of old dogs; it may be accompanied by heart trouble.

The diet is important — raw or lightly cooked meat or fish is most suitable, and not too much at a time.

If the dog is lazy and disinclined to take exercise and is, or has been, subject to skin troubles that may have been suppressed with ointments, etc., then an occasional dose of *Sulphur* 30 will help.

Should it be in poor condition and feel the cold greatly, yet restless and thirsty for frequent small drinks of water and the cough is aggravated by drinking with a suffocative cough and frothy vomit, *Arsenicum* 30, one dose of which should alleviate, or the same remedy in the 3*x* potency three times a day.

Should the dog be worse in a hot room, worse from any excitement or exertion, generally worse after sleep, and hungry, with an improvement of the cough after taking food or drink, then *Spongia* 6 (internally) two- or three-hourly until it improves will keep it happy if given as the need arises.

BAD BREATH

Symptoms: The breath is sometimes very offensive. This is generally due to an accumulation of tartar on the teeth or to decayed teeth, which should be attended to by a veterinary surgeon and scaled, and very decayed teeth removed.

A dose of *Arnica* 30 the day before the appointment will help to heal the mouth after extraction. The mouth can be bathed with *Calendula Lotion* (one

teaspoon of *Calendula* ϕ to a pint of water) after the extractions.

Should the condition be due to a disordered stomach, then *Carbo-Nux* 6, twice a day for a week or so will tone up the digestion.

BALANITIS
Symptoms: Purulent discharge from the prepuce, the dog is irritated and constantly licking the parts.

Give *Merc Sol* 6 morning and evening until there is improvement.

Syringe the passage with *Calendula Lotion* (one teaspoon of *Calendula* φ to one pint of water). This is very soothing and healing; *Calendula* inhibits the growth of micro-organisms.

BILIOUSNESS
Some dogs are given to bilious attacks which are due to liver derangement.

Symptoms: There may be severe vomiting of bile, accompanied by great thirst, and sometimes diarrhoea

Give *Bryonia* 6 and repeat every two hours for a day or two. Starve the dog for 24 hours and then feed on raw or lightly cooked lean meat. Or try *Bryonia* 30 every four hours.

BITES
Punctured wounds caused by the bites of a dog should be bathed with *Calendula Lotion* (one teaspoon of *Calendula* Ø to half a cup of water) and *Ledum* 6 may be given half-hourly, hourly, two-hourly or four-hourly according to the severity of the injury — it prevents sepsis in most cases if given early enough.

BLADDER, INFLAMMATION OR CYSTITIS

Inflammation of the bladder may be caused by exposure to damp and cold, or gravel in the passage may prevent a proper evacuation of the bladder; it may also occur as the result of a dog of clean habits being shut up for a long time, then the bladder becomes over distended, so that it is unable to empty it and inflammation follows.

Symptoms: Restlessness, panting, fullness of the abdomen, evidence of pain and frequent straining to pass water. Blood may be mixed with the water, or be passed in drops after passing the water. The urine may be high coloured and strong smelling.

If the condition is known to be the result of a chill from sitting about in damp weather, give *Rhus Tox* 6, hourly at first and then less frequently.

Should the animal show a dislike for heat in any form, such as warm applications to the bladder (as is often advised), *Apis* 6 should be given every two hours and repeated as needed once improvement is shown. If the urine is *scanty* and *high coloured* and the dog *dislikes heat in any form*, *Apis* is the indicated remedy. If there is *constant straining*, stranguary with *bloody* urine (especially in cases which follow acute diseases) give *Terebinthina* 3 every half-hour and increase the intervals as improvement is shown.

Should stone in the bladder be the cause of the condition and the urine 'runs away in little jets', give *Thlaspi Bur* 3 every half-hour; this often replaces the use of the catheter.

BLOOD POISONING OR SEPTICAEMIA

May arise from the retention of a dead puppy or part of the afterbirth, after effects of miscarriage, from inflammation of the womb, from injuries or following operations.

Symptoms: High temperature and shivering, there may be thirst and vomiting. The dog is very ill indeed.

The cause, if ascertainable, must be removed.

In mild cases, after wounds or operations, *Arnica* 6, hourly for some hours might help.

Should there be restlessness, with low fever, red tongue and thirst for small and frequent drinks, *Arsenicum* 3 four-hourly. Sometimes temperature rises rapidly, but the animal is cold, especially if the injury or operation scar is swollen, discoloured and *dry* and the animal is *very restless*. There may be either obstinate constipation or very offensive diarrhoea, and all discharges are terribly offensive, and the *pulse out of proportion to the temperature*. Then *Pyrogen* 30 will often work a miracle. It can be repeated in four hours if necessary, but it is rapid in action and should not be repeated too frequently.

BLEPHARITIS (Inflamed Eyelids)

Symptoms: The eyelids are sore and crusted. It may be the effect of some acute eye condition, or of Distemper.

Bathe with *Calendula Lotion* (10-12 drops of the φ to a wine glass of water) three times a day and apply a little *Calendula Lotion* to the lids after.

Give *Pulsatilla* 30, one dose every two or three days for a fortnight. When the condition improves, one dose of *Sulphur* 200 will usually complete the cure.

In some chronic cases *Graphites* 30 may be needed in the same way as *Pulsatilla* to clear up the condition. *Graphites* is a great anti-psoric, especially suited to dogs which run to fat, have a tendency to skin troubles and constipation, and are of nervous disposition. There would most likely be moist eruptions elsewhere. It acts particularly well after *Sulphur*.

In chronic cases following some acute disease, *Psorinum* 200 in infrequent doses, might be needed.

BREAST INFLAMMATION
Symptoms: The glands of a suckling bitch sometimes become hard, swollen, red, and painful. There may be a rise in temperature and pus formation (it may be necessary to remove the puppies).

Bathe the parts frequently with a lotion of *Phytolacca* (one teaspoon of φ to one pint of water) and give *Phytolacca* 6, three times a day. *Phytolacca* has a specific action on the breast; it is an 'organ remedy'. This should abort the condition.

If no improvement in 48 hours, bathe with *Calendula Lotion* (ten drops of φ to the ounce of water) and give *Belladonna* 6, two-hourly.

BRONCHITIS

Symptoms: Severe and frequent cough. Difficult breathing, rattling of phlegm. In bad cases the dog sits up as it is afraid to lie down. May be caused by chill, or accompany Distemper.

Keep the dog in a warm room with the window open, out of draughts, and on a light diet if it is willing to eat.

In the early stages *Aconite* 30 four-hourly for three doses may check the disease.

If the dog is thirsty and better lying still, *Bryonia* 6 two-hourly till it shows an improvement.

Should the dog be relieved by a change of position and the attack follows wetting, be very thirsty but refuse any kind of food, *Rhus Tox* 4 would be indicated in the same way.

For bronchial catarrh with wheezing, asthmatic cough, worse in cold air, with profuse expectoration, a suffocative cough, worse in a hot room and with its head low, give *Spongia* 3, two-hourly.

BRUISES

For injuries arising from falls, blows, etc., *where the skin is unbroken* bathe the bruised parts with lotion of *Arnica* (20 drops of ϕ in about half a cup of cold water), or it may be applied on cloths saturated with it.

Give *Arnica* 6 two-hourly and gradually prolong the intervals as improvement is shown.

Should the nerves be injured, use *Hypericum Lotion* (20 drops of ϕ in about half a cup of cold water) and give *Hypericum* 6, two-hourly. This is a wonderful remedy for all such injuries. Excessive painfulness being the guiding symptom for the use of *Hypericum*.

BURNS AND SCALDS

Burns are the result of scorching by fire and scalds by water. In either case, if severe, the hair never grows again.

Apply immediately a sufficiently large piece of warmed cotton wool to cover the burned area so as to exclude all air and bandage to keep this in place. Give *Urtica Urens* 30 every four hours.

If a blister has already formed, be careful not to break it, but apply *Urtica Urens* locally (a teaspoon of ϕ to a pint of water), soak a piece of gauze cloth large enough to cover the area and apply to the burn, cover with cotton wool and bandage. Remove the bandage and cotton wool when the dressing feels dry and re-moisten the gauze cloth with the lotion (without removing it). Continue to give *Urtica Urens* 30 four-hourly, or whenever the dog shows signs of a return of the pain.

In very severe cases, with great pain and restless-ness, *Causticum* 30 may be given instead of *Urtica Urens* and *Hypericum Lotion* applied (a teaspoon of Ø to a pint of water) as described above, being careful *not* to disturb the gauze or cloth on the burn, thus preventing any further injury to the skin.

CALCULI (Stones in the Kidney)
Symptoms: Blood and in other cases pus is passed with the urine. The dog is sometimes very ill with a considerable rise in temperature. There is pain on pressure over the loins, sickness, loss of condition.

In severe cases there may be collapse and death from uraemia.

When there is great pain, the dog cries out and writhes with pain, feeble action of the heart, and the dog must move about. *Dioscorea* 30 every 15 minutes until relief is shown, then at longer intervals as needed. There is generally an aggravation of the condition in the evening and at night and upon lying down, when this remedy (*Dioscorea*) is indicated. The dog prefers to stand and seek the open air.

Thlaspi Bur Ø or 6, every half-hour, often replaces the use of the catheter when there is retention of urine, with frequent desire.

The diet should be light and red meat avoided.

CANCER

A tumour which eventually ulcerates, emitting a very offensive discharge. The animal loses condition and becomes very weak. It can form anywhere but is most commonly found in the mouth, throat, milk glands, the rectum and the abdominal organs.

There appears to be an increase of this disease among animals, as among people.

Cancer is not a local disease, therefore the cure should be constitutional. There are many recorded cases of spontaneous recovery, so that no case need be regarded as hopeless.

As many eminent doctors declare that after an operation when cancer returns, as it usually does, the growth is more rapid and the pain worse, it is far better to avoid an operation, and if the dog is too far gone, to have it painlessly destroyed.

Homoeopathy has many recorded cures of cancer, and it can help a dog so afflicted to enjoy life despite the morbid growth.

Scirrhinum 30 or 200, *Carcinosinum* 30 or 200 in very infrequent doses (once or twice a week) are helpful. *Phosphorus* 30 is invaluable if the animal is thirsty but *vomits the water as soon as it gets warm in the stomach.*

Euphorbia Cor. 30 is most valuable in cases where food, water and mucus are vomited and the attacks occur after short intermissions. One dose as needed.

Silica 30 has often proved to be helpful with obstinate, nervous, chilly dogs with poor appetite, as has *Arsenicum* 30 with restlessness and prostration. *Thuja* 30 would be indicated where there is a history of many inoculations.

Bellis Per 30 where the growth is believed to have been caused by an injury, even should the animal have been injured by a blow or fall years previously.

A diet rich in minerals and vitamins, wholemeal biscuits or rusk are very important adjuncts.

CANKER — See Discharge from Ear

CATARACT
Symptoms: Opaque spots on the pupil of the eye. In old dogs it often starts as a small speck which gradually increases in size. In younger dogs, where it

is uncommon, it increases rapidly; there is gradual loss of vision in the affected eye.

Nat Mur 30 given every two or three days over a period of about two weeks, then left off for a period and repeated in the same way might help in the early stages.

Calc Fluor 6, morning and evening for some weeks has benefited some cases; this should not be continued for too long.

Silica 30 will often clear up an opacity of the eye,

this could be tried in the same way as *Nat Mur* over a long period with occasional intermissions.

Calc Phos 6 is said to check the progress of Cataract, especially indicated if the dog has rheumatism. Give morning and evening.

There is also a cataract resulting from diabetes, the treatment would then be as for Diabetes.

CATARRH OF THE NOSE OR OZOENA

This sometimes follows Distemper. There is a chronic purulent discharge from the nose, which may be offensive.

Give *Pulsatilla* 30 every two or three days for two to three weeks, if no improvement try *Hepar Sulph* 30 in the same way or *Silica* 30, but do not give the last two remedies together.

CHOREA (St. Vitus's Dance)

Symptoms: Spasmodic movements of almost any part of the body. It can arise in a young dog which has grown too fast. Then the remedy is *Phophorus* 30, a dose twice a week for a few weeks.

It is more often a sequel to Distemper and very difficult to cure in bad cases, although it does occasionally clear up spontaneously, in time.

Homoeopathy has had very good results in the treatment of this complaint. According to the side affected:—

Right side: Arsenicum, Causticum, Nat Sulph.

Left side: Cimicifuga, Cuprum or Rhododendron.

Evening aggravation: Zincum met. This is also indicated where exercise improves the case (as it frequently does). Give an occasional dose in the 30th or 200th potency and await results.

Calc Phos 6, *Mag Phos* 6 and *Kali Phos* 6 given consistently often produce gratifying results. These may be taken together and taken over a long period in alternation twice or three times a day.

COLIC

Symptoms: This is met with in puppies as the result of worms, or of eating rubbish. It may also affect older dogs. The dog shows signs of pain by restlessness, crying, whining or howling from severe pain. The abdomen is tucked up and feels hard and rigid. There may be repeated vomiting and diarrhoea. It generally comes on suddenly in a puppy or dog which was previously eating and apparently quite well.

In puppies give *Chamomilla* 30, this may be all that is necessary. Should the stool be green, watery, slimy with soreness of the anus, and bilious vomiting, especially if the trouble arises in teething puppies, *Chamomilla* would be indicated; this may be repeated half-hourly or hourly according to the severity of the attack, and then four-hourly for a few doses as the symptoms abate.

Colocynth 3 may be needed if the pain is *very* distressing, with paroxysms attended by general agitation, and stools dysentric and jelly-like. There may be abdominal distention if *Colocynth* is called for. Give a dose every 15 minutes until relief is shown and then at greater intervals for a few doses.

CONJUNCTIVITIS

Symptoms: The membrane lining the inside of the eye is very congested and dark red, and there is a watery discharge; in bad cases there may be a discharge of pus which sticks the lids together. If neglected, the eye itself may become cloudy and ulcerated.

As a rule this will clear up quickly if the eye be bathed with a lotion of *Euphrasia* (ten to twelve drops of ϕ in a wineglass of warm water); if this strength appears to distress the dog unduly, make a weaker solution. It is better to drop the lotion into the eyes with a medicine dropper, and be sure to wipe each eye after with a fresh piece of cotton wool.

Give *Aconite* 30 hourly for three doses only.

Should the inflammation proceed to ulceration of the cornea, give *Merc Cor* 3 every four hours and bathe with *Calendula* lotion (10 drops of ϕ in a wineglass of warm water) instead of *Euphrasia.*

CONSTIPATION

Symptoms: Big, hard, dry motions, difficult to pass. The dog may go without a motion for several days.

The condition may be caused by unsuitable food and lack of exercise. A change of diet may be necessary.

Treatment:
(1) In mild cases following indigestible food such as too many bones, a few doses of *Nux Vom* 6, after meals will correct the trouble.

(2) In 'bad doers' generally, especially if subject to skin troubles, *Sulphur* 30, once or twice a week for a couple of weeks will often liven up the animal and cure it.

(3) If the animal keeps turning round and seems to have difficulty in evacuating the whole motion, or the

stool when partly expelled recedes again, then *Silica* is the constitutional remedy needed. Give *Silica* 6 three times a day for a week, then a week's rest and then repeat until the condition improves, or *Silica* 30 twice a week.

When constipation alternates with diarrhoea of offensive brownish liquid, and the dog when constipated has large difficult stools, and a sore anus and is timid, given to Blepharitis and inclined to obesity, it needs *Graphites* 30 once or twice a week.

For dogs usually showing 'watery symptoms', as weepy eyes, drooling and slobbering, which are constipated, *Nat Mur* 30, twice a week for a week or two, repeating if the symptoms recur, is suitable.

CONSUMPTION OR TUBERCULOSIS

Symptoms: A rare disease in dogs. A dry cough later becoming loose with expectoration of phlegm, wasting, though the appetite may be reasonably good, and diarrhoea. There is generally a slight rise in temperature round about 102° or a little over (the normal temperature for a dog being 101.4°). This is best taken by inserting an ordinary clinical thermometer in the rectum for half a minute, or a little longer if the dog fidgets.

There may be haemorrhage from the lungs in advanced cases. It can follow a bad case of Pulmonary Distemper or be the result of being fed on T.B. meat.

A dog suffering from Consumption should never be kept with children. If, however, one wishes to give it a chance, it has a fair chance of recovery under Homoeopathic treatment, especially as dogs are resistant to the disease.

If possible, let it live out of doors, and feed liberally on sound, healthy meat, fish, goat's milk and raw eggs.

Give *Tuberculinum* 30 *or Bacillinum* 30 once a week for four weeks, then if the dog responds well, give *Tuberculinum* 100 *or Bacillinum* 100 for another four weeks, and at the end of that time repeat *Tuberculinum* 30 *or Bacillinum* 30 for another four weeks, then stop it.

The other symptoms will require the indicated remedy. Haemorrhage would require *Phosphorus* 30, which need not be repeated unless the symptom recurs. Diarrhoea would need the indicated remedy for the type of diarrhoea. (See heading 'Diarrhoea.')

Should the dog show no improvement after a few doses of *Tuberculinum* or *Bacillnum* there is no use in continuing it.

CONVULSIONS IN PUPPIES

Symptoms: Young puppies, especially during second dentition (from four to six months old), often have convulsions. They may be the result of worms, or of indigestion or over-excitement, particularly on a hot day. The pup which was apparently perfectly well, may suddenly rush about shrieking and looking dazed, or it may suddenly fall on its side, kick its legs, champ its jaws, and froth at the mouth in an epileptiform convulsion; one attack is often followed by others during dentition.

Place the puppy in a dark room for some hours, and keep it quiet. Give it a very light diet for a day or two. Slippery Elm food or milk is quite sufficient.

Treat it for worms if their presence is suspected. Give a dose of *Chamomilla* 30 and repeat in four hours or when necessary.

Convulsions are much more alarming to see than serious, and providing they are due to teething or worms, there is not the least cause to fear that the dog will always be subject to them.

COUGHS

These may arise from various causes, and in a dog that has not had Distemper should be regarded with grave suspicion, as a husky cough is frequently the first symptom of Distemper. If, however, there is no temperature and it arises as the result of a chill, it may be only a form of laryngitis. Keep the dog in an even temperature and out of draughts.

Bryonia 6 given every two hours in alternation with *Belladonna* 6, will generally be all that is necessary. In coughs accompanying heart trouble see 'Heart'.

CUTS

In cases of injury where the dog cuts the skin, *Calendula* φ applied to the cut will check haemorrhage and inhibit the growth of micro-organisms. Arnica 6 or 30 to be given two- to four-hourly for a day or two to allay shock and promote healing.

DANDRUFF

Symptoms: Dryness of the skin and hair; the coat is full of whitish scales, or sometimes brown scales resembling bran.

As a rule a few doses of *Sulphur* 30 given once or twice a day for a few days is all that is necessary to clear up the condition. Give the dog plenty of exercise. A change of diet is sometimes necessary.

DIABETES

Symptoms: Increased secretion of urine of a watery consistency, and thirst. If not treated early, the dog loses condition and gets very thin; but the abdomen is distended and hard owing to the large quantities of water it drinks. Old dogs are very liable to the disease.

In old dogs there is not much hope of a permanent cure. The addition of *Phos Acid* 1x (10 or more drops added to the drinking water) might prove helpful in cases of marked debility, and would be particularly indicated if there were frequent urination at night.

Uranium Nit 30, morning and evening, and then, if there were an improvement in the condition, less frequently, or as required, might help where there is great emaciation, with a tendency to dropsy, vomiting and ravenous appetite.

DIARRHOEA

Symptoms: Frequent loose motions of various types, frequently bloody, sometimes accompanied by sickness and a loss of appetite.

Stop all solid food. If the dog is in good condition, starve it for at least 24 hours and then feed on Slippery Elm food or Arrowroot made with milk.

Small offensive, frequent motions, often containing blood, with much prostration, worse after midday or midnight (generally between 1 or 2 a.m. or p.m.), dysenteric stools, with the dog wanting warmth, and with thirst and restlessness, call for *Arsenicum* 6, every two or three hours.

Whitish-grey, greenish or bloody and *slimy* stools with a lot of straining, worse in the evening, will call for *Mer Cor* 6, every two hours until relieved.

'No two stools alike' calls for *Pulsatilla* 6 or 30,

two- to four-hourly until relieved.

Frothy painless stools, diarrhoea of blood and slime, *after getting wet*, try *Rhus Tox* 6, two-hourly.

Stool *green*, watery like chopped eggs and spinach, soreness of anus, the diarrhoea met with in teething puppies, needs *Chamomilla* 30, and repeat, if necessary, in four hours or as needed.

Painless, copious debilitating diarrhoea, green mucus with grains like sago with *great weakness*, calls for *Phosphorus* 30, and repeat, if necessary, in four hours or as needed.

If stools are accompanied with colicky pain, each paroxysm attended with great agitation, puppy cries and head stretched forward, especially should the attack occur when 'the air is cold, but the sun still hot enough to heat the blood', the dog would respond to *Colcynth* 30; repeat, if necessary, in four hours or as needed.

After a prolonged attack of diarrhoea it is advisable to give the dog a dose of *China* 6, morning and evening for a week or two to overcome the debility from the loss of vital fluids.

N.B. In simple cases of diarrhoea a change of diet may be all that is necessary. Raw meat will often cure the condition if it be due to an unsuitable diet.

DISCHARGE FROM EAR (CANKER)

Symptoms: The inside of the ear may be red and painful. The dog scratches its ear and may shake its head, rub it and carry it to one side in bad cases. In slight cases there is a brown discharge, in more severe cases the discharge may be liquid, purulent and very offensive.

In mild cases there may just be an accumulation of wax; the ear should be cleaned out with cotton wool (a fresh piece for each ear) until no more brown discharge is apparent on the wool, then a little *Calendula Ointment* applied on the cotton wool to each ear.

If there be a yellow, fetid discharge, *worse at night* and worse for warmth, (1) give *Merc Sol* 6, morning and evening for a week or two. (2) With scurf behind the ear, in unthrifty dogs subject to skin affections and glandular swellings, give *Hepar Sulph Calcareum* 30, one dose every two or three days for two or three weeks; this would be particularly suitable to an irritable dog and one that cannot bear to have the ear touched. (3) *Pulsatilla* 30 given in the same way might suit a rather timid, amiable, gentle yet obstinate dog better, followed by *Silica* 30 at the same intervals (*Silica* is the chronic of *Pulsatilla*). (4) For ill-smelling discharge, with eczema around the ears, in a chilly dog, which nevertheless is *always very hungry,* give *Psorinum* 30, one dose every two or three days for two or three weeks. (5) *Tellurium* 30 works wonderfully well in catarrh of the middle ear with an acrid discharge smelling like fish brine, and suits a sensitive dog. The dog seems to have pains all over it and is afraid to be touched. It may be subject to eczema.

DISTEMPER

Symptoms: The first symptom of Distemper is a rise of temperature, but this is very often missed, and the disease has often progressed to the secondary stage before the condition is noticed. Most young dogs are subject to this complaint, although it can attack older dogs, but these have generally developed an immunity to it, and there are some dogs that have a natural immunity to the disease and never get it. Others survive without its presence having been detected, until the typical 'Distemper teeth' erupt and are proof that they have had it prior to the second dentition.

If your dog is off its food, dull, disinclined for exercise, take the temperature at once (it is best to take it in the rectum) and if there be a rise of temperature to 103 or more, isolate the dog at once, and you may prevent the disease from spreading. If it is Distemper, other symptoms will develop. indeed, they are often the first to be observed, such as a husky cough (which, to the uninitiated, is often mistaken for a choke), there may be diarrhoea, sickness, sore eyes and a thick nasal discharge; or there may be none of these symptoms and the first apparent symptom may, in cases of Hard Pad, which is only a more virulent form of Distemper, be fits and meningitis, which show that the nervous system is affected and then the case is almost hopeless.

When the first malaise with a rise in temperature, *thirst* and *restlessness* be noticed, *Aconite* 30, three doses in all at intervals of four hours, may be all that is required to check its progress; however, this stage is seldom observed.

Should the dog be shaky and prostrated with catarrhal symptoms and an inflamed throat, but with no thirst, give *Gelsemium* 30, four-hourly for a few doses.

If these fail to check the disease, give *Distemperinum* 30 morning and evening from the first and all through the course of the disease. Other medicines as indicated by the symptoms should be given while the temperature keeps above normal.

For the cough give *Bryonia* 6, two-hourly; bathe the eyes, if very sore and mattery, with a lotion of *Euphrasia* or *Calendula* (10 or 12 drops of ϕ to one wineglass of water).

If the temperature keeps up, give *Ferrum Phos* 30, four-hourly.

In cases starting with pinky diarrhoea and very rapid prostration, with the animal chilly and the skin having a dried-up look, the disease is probably Hard Pad, and can sometimes be checked by *Arsenicum* 200, one dose.

The diet is very important, it should consist of fluids only while the temperature is high. The dog that eats voraciously is very likely to develop meningitis; but let it have as much water to drink as it wants. It is much better with house-trained dogs — no matter how ill they may be, even with Pneumonia — to carry them out to the garden about three or four times a day, and put them down, keeping them on the lead, let them relieve themselves, and carry them back to their sick quarters after.

They only distress themselves if they are kept in. It is, of course, advisable in cold weather to put a coat on the dog for this purpose.

No exercise beyond this should be allowed as it is likely to induce fits.

For other complications following Distemper, see Chorea, Paralysis, Fits, Pneumonia and Bronchitis.

DISTEMPER (PREVENTION OF)
The Homoeopathic nosode *Distemperinum* is a very efficient preventative of Distemper. It can safely be given to puppies from six weeks old and it appears to act well in any potency. There are never any ill effects.

At six weeks old start giving one dose of *Distemperinum* 30 twice a week for four weeks. This may be repeated at any time if an outbreak of Distemper is known to be in the neighbourhood, or if the dog is to be shown, or likely to be exposed to infection.

DROPSY

This is, as a rule, the result of heart or kidney disease. An enlarged liver may also be a cause.

The limbs may become swollen as well as the abdomen. The fluid can be detected by placing the hand on one side of the stomach and then tapping the other side, when the fluid may be felt like a bladder full of water. The dog becomes thin about the neck and chest and the muscles waste. The breathing may be distressed and the dog walks with difficulty.

In old dogs there is not much hope of permanent relief.

(1) With absence of thirst *Apis* 3*x* two-hourly might be helpful.

(2) With thirst and albumin in the urine *Arsenicum* 3, two-hourly.

(3) Dropsy from diseases of the liver might be relieved by *Apocynum Can* 3*x*, a dose morning and evening. The Dropsy is characterised by great thirst and gastric irritability. *A diminished frequency of the pulse is a prime indication* for this remedy, but it needs to be administered with care and stopped at once should its administration be followed by severe vomiting and signs of collapse.

DYSENTERY

Symptoms: Frequent liquid motions of mucus and blood with severe straining. There may be vomiting and thirst.

Give *Merc Corr* 6 every two hours, this may be alternated with *Colocynth* 6 if there is much colic.

If there be vomiting and much straining, give *Ipecacuanha* 6, two-hourly.

DYSPEPSIA (OR INDIGESTION)

Some dogs seem to be born with a weak digestion, others acquire it as the result of food unsuitable either in quantity or quality.

Symptoms: The appetite is either fussy or insatiable; the bowels may be at times loose or constipated; there may be vomiting after food. The tongue is a dark red colour, showing that there is an inflammatory condition of the digestive organs.

The diet is important. Meat is the natural food for a dog and it is best given raw (if one can be sure that it is sound and not diseased). Should there be any doubt as to its quality, it is better to cook it.

As worms will upset the digestion, make sure the dog is free of them, but many dogs have their digestions upset by unnecessary worming.

A few days on a very light diet such as Slippery Elm food made with milk will soothe the digestive organs; this should be followed for a while by a diet of meat only.

Give Carbo-Nux 6 after meals for a week or more.

In case of acidity and worms, *Nat Phos* 6x, two or three times a day for some long period of weeks will often cure indigestion and remove the worms.

ECZEMA

This is a non-contagious skin disease.

Symptoms: The dog scratches and licks itself. The skin is dry and scaly in dry eczema. Wet eczema exudes a serous fluid and the dog scratches and bites and licks the irritable parts and moist red sores appear. The parts principally affected are the ears, along the back, near the root of the tail, but any part may become affected.

It may be caused by lack of exercise and unsuitable diet. It is often hereditary.

A change of diet is sometimes all that is necessary, from a farinaceous to a meat diet, or if the dog is being fed on fish, give it meat instead. See that it gets plenty of free exercise in the open air.

Most cases respond to *Sulphur*. This is specially indicated in constitutional cases which crop up every time the dog starts coating, or which recur every spring. One dose of *Sulphur* 200, to be repeated in a week or two, is generally sufficient to check the attack. Dogs with dry, lack-lustre coats generally need and respond well to *Sulphur* in any potency.

Should skin troubles arise after any acute disease, the administration of *Psorinum* 200 would be indicated. It should be tried when there is no reaction to the usual remedies, especially if the dog is particularly sensitive to cold. A greedy dog, with skin trouble, would be likely to benefit by *Psorinum* — but it should not be repeated too often. Three doses at intervals of a week are sufficient as a rule to bring about a reaction. If there is no benefit from this do not repeat, but try *Sulphur* as indicated above.

Dogs with a dry, rough scaly skin which *feel the cold greatly* would need *Arsenicum* 6, a dose morning or evening for a week at a time. Another indication for *Arsenicum* would be that the dog is *worse in wet weather.*

The dog which, in addition to eczematous eruptions with intense itching shows rheumatic tendencies, and is better moving about, but worse in cold and rainy weather, needs *Rhus Tox — a dose in the 30th* potency once or twice a week.

Dogs with Eczema discharging a glutinous fluid, sticky, with a rough dry skin, accompanied by Blepharitis (eczema of the eyelids) and eruptions around the mouth and chin, should be given *Graphites* 30 — a dose every two or three days for some time.

ENTERITIS

Symptoms: This often commences with vomiting. There is often a rise of temperature, the pulse is more rapid, with pain on pressure of abdomen. There may be either diarrhoea or constipation. The dog appears to be ill and is disinclined to move. Generally there is loss of appetite, but considerable thirst.

The diet should be strictly fluid. Let the dog drink water if it wants to; it may also have milk, or Slippery Elm food, which is very soothing.

(1) With great prostration, yet with restlessness, *coated tongue with red edges*, loose stools which are *very offensive*, and may be thin, dark and bloody, throat inflamed, with no appetite, but constant desire for water — *Baptisia* 3x two-hourly should be given.

(2) If there is great and rapid prostration, and the stools very small, offensive and dark and may be bloody, and the dog is thirsty but only takes a lap or two at a time, give *Arsenicum* 6 every two hours. A dry, clean and red tongue would be an indication for *Arsenicum*.

(3) With constipation, worse on movement, thirst for large quantities of water, vomiting of bile and water, and the tongue coated yellow or dark brown or white, with dryness of the mouth, give *Bryonia* 6 every two hours.

If the dog does not respond to remedies and appears to be past help, then try *Pyrogen* 30, which may be given four-hourly and has often wrought miracles.

EPILEPSY

Symptoms: Dogs are often subject to Epilepsy or to spileptiform fits. An attack is generally sudden, the dog may be going along quite happily, it may (or may not) cry out, then suddenly fall on its side, champ its jaws, froth at the mouth and become unconscious. The attack does not, as a rule, last long, and when the dog recovers consciousness it looks about in a dazed manner and if not restrained will probably rush off.

One attack is often followed by another, so put the dog in a secure place, preferably darkened, and keep it quiet. Should an attack occur while out at exercise, put the lead on the dog while it is unconscious, so as to prevent it bolting upon recovering consciousness. These attacks are exhausting to the dog and are generally followed by profound sleep. Immediately upon recovering consciousness, a dog might snap at its owner, this is simply because it is not yet properly conscious and does not recognise him, so it is as well to handle it carefully at that stage of the attack.

If the attacks follow distemper, they are not very likely to be cured permanently, although if they are infrequent, there may be fewer attacks as time goes on. Some nervous dogs seem to be predisposed to various forms of fits, and a careful diet, avoiding biscuit meal or too large a meal, helps to diminish the attacks. Epileptiform convulsions in teething puppies are unlikely to recur once the dentition is complete.

Immediately after an attack give *Belladonna* 6 every two hours for a few doses — this may prevent another. In fat scrofulous dogs, *Calc Carb* 6 every eight hours might help. In thin dogs *Calc Phos* 6 every eight hours. Dogs needing Calcium in some form or other are generally nervous. Fits *during sleep* might be helped by *Silica* 6 every eight hours. An occasional dose of *Sulphur* 200 might help if fits should follow suppression of skin symptoms.

There are other remedies to be called for according to the probable cause of the attacks; but chronic and probably hereditary cases do not respond very readily to any treatment.

FEET (Cysts)

Symptoms: The dog is observed to be licking and biting at its foot, which is red and inflamed. Often an abscess forms which is exceedingly painful — sometimes it affects both feet, or one after the other.

(1) If the ulcer is very sensitive to contact give *Hepar Sulph* 6 every three hours.

(2) In long lasting cases, especially in chilly dogs, which may be nervous and fearful, give *Silica* 6 every three hours instead.

(3) When the cyst is cured, give the dog a course of *Sulphur* 30 — a dose every day for one week and then one dose of *Sulphur* 200 or 1m.

Externally, *Calendula Lotion* (10 drops of φ to half a wineglass of water) will rapidly allay the irritation.

FITS — See Convulsions and Epilepsy, Hysteria.

FLATULENCE

Symptoms: Simple flatulence may arise in dogs with a weak digestion, when all that is needed is a light diet, to be followed by a course of *Carbo-Nux* 6 (see Dyspepsia). Sometimes, however, puppies or adult dogs become distended with gas, the abdomen is enormously swollen and hard, the dog breathes with difficulty and it may slobber and attempt to vomit. There is great prostration and tendency to collapse, and if not rapidly relieved the animal dies.

Puppies seem more often to be affected at night.

Give *Colchicum* 3x, repeat in 10 to 15 minutes until relief is obtained. Keep the animal warm and quiet and on a light diet for some days. If need be, give a few doses of *Arnica* 6 to overcome the effect of the shock. (Incidentally, there are recorded cases of *Colchicum* rendering unnecessary the use of the knife in cows similarly affected.)

FRACTURES

Fractures need skilled veterinary attention. While awaiting this it will help the effect of shock to administer *Arnica* 6 immediately and to repeat this from one- to four-hourly, according to the severity of the shock.

This should be followed about 24 hours later, to promote union of the fracture, by *Symphytum* 1x every four hours, until the bone is set. These remedies not only add to the patient's comfort, but expedite healing.

For compound fractures, with much injury to the nerves, *Hypericum* 6, one hourly, is the remedy *par excellence.* For punctured wounds do not forget *Ledum* 6, one hourly.

GASTRITIS (Inflammation of the Stomach)

Symptoms: Frequent, and sometimes violent, vomiting, sometimes accompanied by diarrhoea. There may be great thirst.

(1) If the tongue be red and the dog very prostrated, yet restless and thirsty, but apparently afraid to drink much because it feels so sick, the motions very small and very offensive, and sometimes bloody, give *Arsenicum* 6 every two hours.

(2) With thirst for cold water which is vomited *as soon as it gets warm in the stomach*, the tongue *dry* either red or white but *not* thickly coated, give *Phosphorus* 6 *or* 30 — two- to four-hourly.

(3) With tongue yellowish coated, dry lips, better lying still; great thirst — vomiting of bile, stools brown, thick or bloody, *Bryonia* 6 *or* 30, two- to four-hourly, should be given.

Withhold all food for at least 24 hours and then feed on small quantities of Slippery Elm food made with milk at four-hourly intervals. Bring the dog slowly back to its normal diet.

GOITRE

Symptoms: A swelling, varying in size, situated low down on the neck, due to an enlargement of the thyroid gland. As a rule it does not appear to cause much inconvenience to the dog.

(1) In emaciated dogs, with voracious appetite and

considerable restlessness, try *Iodine* 3x every four hours.

(2) In fat, soft animals, especially if the gland be very hard, *Calc Carb* 6 morning and evening or *Calc Fluor* 6 in the same way over a period might help.

(3) With frequent hiccough, thirst, great hunger with a dry croupy cough, larynx sensitive to touch, generally worse after sleep — *Spongia* 3 every four hours for some considerable time would be indicated.

HOEMATOMA (Ear)

Symptoms: There is a swelling of blood or serum under the skin or inside of the flap of the ear; this is very painful, causing the dog to hold its head to one side and cry out if it is touched. It is due to an injury or blow to the flap of the ear which causes a breakdown of small blood vessels between the skin and cartilage. It is something induced as a result of canker and resultant scratching.

If attended to early, the swelling may be dispersed by bathing with *Calendula Lotion* (10 to 12 drops of Ø to half a wineglass of water) and *Arnica* 6-30, three or four times daily. If the swelling does not go down in two or three days, then an operation is the only cure.

HEART DISEASE

Affections of the heart are not uncommon among dogs, especially among the toy breeds.

Symptoms: Difficulty of breathing after exertion, sometimes fainting. There may be a dry cough. Attacks are sometimes induced in very hot weather. Digestive troubles will often aggravate the condition. At times there is evidence of great pain and the dog is very restless.

Keep the dog quiet. Avoid hard exercise and feed on meat.

For the dry cough of organic heart trouble, give *Spongia* 30, a dose as needed. (See Asthma.)

Crataegus in almost any potency is of great value in any heart affection, it is a wonderful heart tonic and will often keep old dogs with heart trouble happy for a long time. Extreme breathlessness upon exertion, *irregular feeble and intermittent pulse, and aggravation from warmth* are indications of *Crataegus.* It can be given in the mother tincture 4-8 hourly or in the 30 potency when necessary.

HYSTERIA
Symptoms: Hysteria is an unpleasant disease but it seldom, if ever, proves fatal, or leaves any after effects. Its cause is unknown. In some cases it is induced by certain foods, when the cure is obvious. In other cases there is no apparent cause. It was — in the U.S.A. — known as 'fright disease', not unsuitably, as the dog seems to be frightened. The attacks come on suddenly; the dog might, out at exercise, suddenly rush off screaming, as in puppy teething fits. It is temporarily quite unconscious; if possible, it

is far better to leave it alone in a safe place until it recovers its senses and then to put it in a quiet, safe, darkened kennel or room, and keep it there for a period of three weeks, during which time the attacks are liable to recur. In other cases the dog has fits resembling epilepsy, but these, unlike true epilepsy, cease when the attack is over.

If there be any fear of the attacks being caused by diet, then change the diet. Some dogs wolf their food and will induce an attack, then it is probably no more than acute indigestion. It is better to feed on fish or meat only for some days following an attack, and during the attack to *withhold all solid food*, but allow the dog plenty of water. For the fear give *Aconite* 30, one dose, and do not be in a hurry to repeat it. In young excitable puppies, *Belladonna* 6 every two or three hours for a couple of days is helpful — or *Chamomilla* 30 every four hours in the same way.

As a rule dogs subject to Hysteria do better if one avoids all biscuit meal and even bread, and feeds them on raw flaked oats, barley or maize, or any breakfast cereal previously soaked with gravy or milk, fed cool, with fish or meat.

HOMESICKNESS

Some dogs are very homesick when they are left in boarding kennels or parted from their owners. They fret and refuse their food despite kind treatment.

As a rule a few doses of *Ignatia* 30 will pacify them and reconcile them to their new surroundings. Old dogs which are peevish and sulky and sensitive to cold in similar conditions might respond to *Capsicum* 30. Often one dose suffices, or it can be repeated 4-hourly.

INDIGESTION — See Dyspepsia.

INSECT BITES
Some dogs will snap at wasps and bees and get stung. The parts get very much swollen and painful.

Give (1) *Apis* 3x two-hourly, when there is a sudden puffing up. (2) *Ledum* 6 two-hourly. If the wounded part is cold, *Ledum* would be indicated.

JAUNDICE (Congestion of the Liver)
May be caused by a chill, or due to the infection of the duct with a bile stone.

Certain forms of infectious Jaundice are carried by rats.

Symptoms: It is pretty deadly in dogs and often is not recognised for what it is. There is sickness, depression, loss of appetite, and generally obstinate constipation. The urine is scanty and high coloured. The mucous membranes, skin and whites of the eyes get more yellow as the disease progresses.

In Leptospirosis, spread by rat urine, the disease appears in two forms; there is an unsteady elevation of the temperature, nausea, lassitude, loss of weight, loose stools and stiffness. The vomit and stools may be bloody in the icterohaemorrhagic type.

For Jaundice which is the result of chill, *Merc Sol* 6 four-hourly. *Chelidonium* 3x may be alternated with the *Merc Sol.* Give rabbit broth in which dandelion leaves have been boiled with rusks of stale brown bread. Avoid all fats. Milk and soda water may be retained when nothing else is, and later boiled fish.

Bryonia 6 two-hourly should help where there is much thirst and warm drinks aggravate the nausea.

The disease may have progressed so far that serious damage has been done to the liver and kidneys by the time the yellow discoloration appears. The disease is difficult to identify at an early stage, and is frequently mistaken for some form of distemper until it has progressed too far to cure. *If the temperature fluctuates markedly from very high to almost normal leptospirosis should be suspected.*

In malignant Jaundice, *Phosphorus* 3, two-hourly, and in the icterohaemorrhagic type, with blood in the vomit and stools, *Crotalus Horr* 3 two-hourly might help.

KIDNEYS (Inflammation — NEPHRITIS)

An acute attack generally comes on suddenly, may be caused by a chill, or may be the result of stone in the kidneys. There is pain over the loins, and the dog walks with difficulty and with its back arched. There is a rise in temperature, the pulse is quickened, the urine is high coloured, and there may be indications of dropsy. The dog is thirsty and is frequently sick.

If the result of a chill give:—

(1) *Aconite* 6 at two-hourly intervals.

(2) If no improvement give *Belladonna* 3 hourly.

(3) With suppression of urine and *constant urging to urinate, give Cantharis* 3 hourly.

(4) With blood in urine, *Terebinthina* 3 hourly is indicated.
Thlaspi Bur 6 every 15 minutes should help, it is indicated where 'the urine runs away in little jets'.

In chronic cases with prostration, anxiety, thirst, chilliness, the tongue dry, clean and red, *Arsenicum* 3 two-hourly often helps.

Diet is important. Red meat should be avoided, but tripe (or uncleaned paunch with all fat removed) or fish may be given with rice or any breakfast cereals or rusked brown bread.

LACTATION (Disorders of)
Undue engorgement of breasts sometimes occurs, making it difficult, if not impossible, for the pups to suckle. Give *Bryonia* 3 two-hourly.

When the milk is poor in quality in lazy, fat bitches, give *Calc Carb* 6 three times a day.

In thin rickety bitches, give *Silica* 6 three times a day.

In debility following lactation, give *China* 3 two-hourly for a couple of weeks. This is a wonderful remedy for debility from exhausting discharges, or loss of vital fluids from whatever cause.

Where there is a deficiency of milk remember *Alfalfa* φ. This will increase the quantity and quality of milk in nursing bitches. Ten drops in milk, three times daily, will help.

In some cases maiden bitches get a large secretion of milk, at the time they would usually have produced it if mated. The bitch becomes restless and unhappy, she will behave as if she were about to have puppies, scratching up her bedding and generally behaving like a bitch about to whelp. *Pulsatilla* 3 four-hourly will diminish the flow of milk. Should this be insufficient, give five drops of *Urtica Urens* φ in a little water four-hourly, which will arrest the flow.

LARYNGITIS
Inflammation of the throat, probably due to a chill.

Symptoms: A dry teasing cough, the dog will sometimes retch as if about to vomit.

Give *Aconite* 30 at four-hourly intervals for three doses. This will generally clear up the condition.

Keep the dog dry and warm, in an even temperature for a few days. In bad cases an inhalation of

Friar's Balsam may relieve.

If *Aconite* does not clear up all the symptoms, the dog has a dry, croupy cough, which *improves after eating or drinking*, give *Spongia* 1x two-hourly for a few days.

LUMBAGO
This is a form of rheumatism affecting the loins. The dog shows signs of considerable pain when it moves or if one applies pressure to the loins. Badly affected dogs may temporarily lose the use of their hind legs.

Give *Rhus Tox* 30 in alteration with *Bryonia* 30 four-hourly.

LUNGS (Inflammation of)
Symptoms: This is not a common complaint in dogs apart from Distemper, but it can occur as the result of a bad chill or neglected cough. The attack generally begins with shivering, the temperature rises to 103° or higher, and pulse is increased in frequency. The breathing is quick. The dog may have a husky cough, it is off its food and the eyes are congested.

At the commencement after a chill from exposure to a sudden cold spell, *Aconite* 30, three doses at hourly intervals, may check it.

Bryonia 6, two- to four-hourly, in alternation with *Phosphorus* 6, for the cough.

In Broncho-pneumonia, with *great rattling of mucus*, with rapid short difficult breathing, the dog sits up till it sinks with exhaustion, as it fears it will suffocate, give *Ant Tart* 30, four-hourly. Should there be no improvement in 48 hours, try *Lycopodium* 30 in the same way; if the cough is worse at night, with great breathlessness and flaying of the alae nasal, this would be an indication for *Lycopodium*.

With great prostration, thirst, anxiety and restlessness, *Arsenicum* 3, two-hourly, would be indicated.

The diet should be light: milk, glucose in water, honey and water, eggs and milk laced with brandy, meat extracts, Slippery Elm food. The room should be warm, with plenty of fresh air, but free from draughts.

MANGE (Sarcoptic)
Symptoms: This disease, which is caused by a parasite, is contagious both to other animals and to people. It usually starts around the eyes, ears, the elbows and outside of the hind legs. The skin is reddened and the dog is constantly scratching, which further aggravates the condition. If neglected, it spreads to other parts of the body, and the dog loses condition rapidly from lack of rest. Warmth in any form increases the irritation.

This complaint is easily cured, but the animal should — because of the risk of contagion — be isolated and all suspected contacts should be given a protective bath. A sulphur solution bath (2 ozs. of sulphurated potash to 1 gallon of water) at weekly intervals for about three weeks usually is enough to effect a cure. The interval is to allow any eggs that have been unaffected by the bath to hatch out. All toilet articles, collars and leads should be disinfected after use, and bedding burned or sprayed with 40 per cent Formaldehyde solution. The spray penetrates all cracks and crevices, and is harmless to furniture and fabrics too. The dog should not be put back into its kennel until the spray has dried, as it gives off fumes. When giving the dog a sulphur bath, the solution must reach every part; though great care should be taken that it does not get into the eyes. Do not rinse the dog but dry thoroughly and see that it is quite dry before returning it to its quarters.

Give one dose of *Sulphur* 200 once a week, or *Sulphur* 6 morning and evening till cured.

MANGE (Follicular)
This skin complaint is confined for the most part to puppies, though adult dogs occasionally get it. It is *not* contagious to people and less so to other animals than Sarcoptic Mange, and not all dogs appear to be susceptible to it.

Symptoms: Follicular Mange is a progressive disease. It often commences with a small circular bare patch on the dog's face, though the patch may appear elsewhere. The patch is generally greyish with a few red pimples or elevations of the skin. Some of these places contain a blood coloured fluid, or there may be mattery spots. The fluid contains the parasite.

As the disease progresses, the original patch increases and runs into other patches. The skin looks dry and corrugated, and the hair falls off and often fails to grow again. The skin turns blue-black or dark grey.

The dog does not scratch much, but shakes itself and looks most unthrifty.

The disease is much commoner in the short-haired than in the long-haired dogs.

The dog should be isolated in the kennel and all grooming appliances, collars, leads, etc., disinfected as previously advised. Never give dogs subject to this disease straw bedding.

There are now, I understand, external preparations that can cure this complaint.

Internally, give a weekly dose of *Sulphur* 200.

It would be wise never to breed from an animal which has been subject to the complaint, as there would appear to be a hereditary predisposition to the trouble.

MARASMUS
Symptoms: Loss of condition without apparent cause, emaciation, anaemia.

Diet is important. Feed on good sound raw meat,

wholemeal biscuit. Exercise in open air.

Give 10 drops of *Alfalfa* φ in a little water three times a day.

Very often *Sulphur* in the higher potencies as 200 or 1m will alter the whole picture, particularly if the coat should be dry and lack lustre, given in infrequent doses. One dose is usually enough to improve the condition.

MASTITIS (Inflammation of the Breast)

Symptoms: This is not uncommon in nursing bitches. The breast is tender, red and swollen. The bitch may go off her food and have a rise of temperature. Often an abscess forms.

Bathe the parts frequently with warm *Calendula Lotion* (one teaspoonful of φ to half to three-quarters of a tumbler of water).

In the early symptoms of pain and hardness, give *Bryonia* 6 three-hourly; this sometimes clears up the condition.

Should *Bryonia* fail in 48 hours, give *Phytolacca* 6 every two hours and bathe with *Phytolacca Lotion* in place of *Calendula* (10 drops of φ to a wineglass of water).

If the parts are red and inflamed, yet less hard, give *Belladonna* 6 every hour or two-hourly.

If an abscess should form, bathe with *Calendula*

Lotion and give *Hepar Sulph* 6 every three hours.

Phytolacca (Poke Root) is much used in America to disperse inflammatory enlargements of the udders and to regulate abnormalities in the milk of cows.

MUMPS
Although there have been cases of puppies which contracted Mumps as a result of being handled by their owners who had the complaint, these are very unusual.

Dogs not infrequently develop a large swelling below the ear as a result of inflammation of the Parotid gland. It often comes up quite suddenly; the dog is sorry for itself, and there may be a rise of temperature and loss of appetite.

Bathe with warm *Calendula Lotion* (one teaspoon-ful of ϕ to half a tumbler of water) and give *Tarentula Cub* 30 every four hours. After the bulk of the discharge has come away replace the lotion with *Calendula Ointment.*

NAILS (Dew Claws)
Dew claws should be removed from the hind legs of most breeds a few days after birth by being cut close to the leg with sharp curved scissors. It is usual these days to remove the dew claws from the fore legs, too. They are of no use, but can do much harm if the dog scratches its eyes. They also sometimes grow into the flesh and cause trouble in that way.

Apply pure *Calendula* ϕ to the cuts. This will

arrest any haemorrhage.

NASAL POLYPUS
Symptoms: The dog breathes oddly, as if there were an obstruction in its nose, as the result of a narrow-necked growth in the nasal passage. There may be a discharge from the nose accompanying the complaint.

Give *Thuja* 30, one dose daily for a week or so.

NECROSIS (Diseased Bone)
Symptoms: Following an injury or operation an abscess sometimes forms owing to bits of dead bone remaining behind.

Bathe with *Calendula Lotion* (one teaspoonful of φ to half tumbler of water), and give *Silica 3x*, one dose three times a day for a week or more (this promotes the expulsion of foreign bodies from the tissues).

NETTLERASH (Urticaria)
This may be the result of a chill or (in susceptible dogs) of indigestion. The skin becomes swollen and lumpy; the head is often very swollen.

It generally passes off quite quickly.

Some puppies get it during second dentition.

If the attack be due to a chill, give *Aconite* 30; one or two doses may be all that is necessary.

The dog should be kept warm and on a low diet for

a few days.

If there is much swelling a few doses of *Apis* 3x, every two hours, will reduce it.

NEURALGIA
Symptoms: Dogs are sometimes affected by Neuralgia in the muscles and nerves of the neck and shoulders. The pain comes on suddenly and the dog will cry out. The muscles may be swollen and tense, and the dog moves slowly and stiffly.

If following exposure to cold draughts, give *Aconite* 30 for two or three doses (not more); if this does not relieve the pain, give *Belladonna* 30 every four hours.

NIPPLES, SORE
Symptoms: When a bitch has been suckling her puppies for some weeks, the nipples may become inflamed and cracked, so that she objects to the puppies drawing her milk.

Bathe with *Calendula Lotion* (one teaspoonful of φ to half tumbler of water).

OBESITY (Fatness)
Obesity is commoner in some breeds than in others. It may be due to lack of exercise and unsuitable diet, when the remedy is obvious; it is not always so.

A greedy dog which is fat should be given raw meat

only in small quantities and nothing else except water and plenty of free exercise, which is often all that is necessary to reduce its weight. Allow no food between meals.

The internal administration of *Phytolacca Berry* φ tablets every eight hours is often used in the treatment of obesity. It should be given for three to four weeks. *Nat Mur* 30 and *Nat Phos* 30 twice a week sometimes help.

ORCHITIS (Inflammation of the Testicles)

This may arise as the result of an injury or from constitutional causes. The testicles become swollen and painful. The dog walks and sits down with difficulty.

If due to injury, give *Arnica* 6 every two hours for some time.

Acute cases may be relieved by *Pulsatilla* 30 four-hourly, with thick yellow discharge and difficulty in passing water, or *Belladonna* 30 four-hourly if the testicles are hard and inflamed.

Local compresses of *Hamamelis* (a teaspoonful of φ to half a pint of water) affords relief.

In old dogs with chronic inflammation, especially if this complaint should be accompanied by cough, *Spongia* 3 two-hourly, should help.

OPHTHALMIA

Symptoms: The conjunctival membrane is very inflamed, with a flow of tears from the eyes, which may go on to a purulent discharge.

There is intolerance of light, so that the eyes are kept shut or partly so.

Keep the dog in a darkened room, avoid glaring lights and draughts. Bathe frequently with warm *Euphrasia Lotion* (10 drops of φ to a wineglass of water, or weaker if the dog objects).

Give *Aconite* 3x hourly at first for about six doses; if no better and there is great fear of light, give *Belladonna* 3x in alternation with *Pulsatilla* 3x four-hourly.

If there be much purulent discharge, bathe with *saline solution* (one teaspoonful of salt to a pint of water) and smear the eyelids with *Calendula Ointment* afterwards to prevent them sticking together.

In obstinate cases, due to constitutional causes in unthrifty animals, *Aethiops* 4x three hourly.

Care must be taken to prevent the dog from scratching the eyes and it should have its dew claws bandaged to prevent this or to be made to wear a wide cardboard collar to prevent it from rubbing the eyes with its paws.

Calendula Lotion (20 drops of φ to a teacupful of water) is excellent in chronic affections of the eyelids.

OZOENA — See Catarrh.

PARALYSIS
This is not uncommon in dogs. Sometimes all the legs are affected, at other times only the hind legs are paralysed. It is a fairly common sequel to Distemper or it may be the result of injury to the spine or head. It may be occasioned by Rheumatism.

The dog should not be allowed always to lie on the

same side.

In cases known to be the result of injury, give *Arnica* 6 two-hourly at first and *Arnica Lotion* (one teaspoonful of ϕ to half a cup of water) applied to the spine two or three times a day. Later *Arnica* 30 morning and evening should replace *Arnica* 6.

If there be no improvement in a week or so and if the spine is very sensitive to the touch and the dog is sensitive to cold, give *Hypericum* 1x three or four times a day, and bathe the spine with *Hypericum Lotion* (one part of ϕ to 25 parts of water).

Should the paralysis follow Distemper, or if there have been many injections, one dose of *Thuja* 1m should be given as an antidote.

If the paralysis is worse in wet weather or is affected by rain, give *Rhus Tox* 30 four-hourly.

Where the dog's skin is very rough and matted and it feels the cold very much, *Psorinum* 1m, one dose only may help.

If the back is hot to the touch, *Phosphorus* 6 four-hourly.

Gelsemium 30 is often useful in cases following Distemper with complete prostration. Give internally night and morning for two or three weeks.

Should paralysis follow convulsions, give *Hyoscy-*

amus 30 every two or three days for two or three weeks.

Distemperinum 30, a dose night and morning for a week, might be of help in stubborn cases.

If the paralysis is the result of rheumatism, *Rhus Tox* 30, alternated with *Bryonia* 30, a dose every four hours, will help.

PARTURIENT ECLAMPSIA

Symptoms: This occurs in nervous bitches about two or three weeks after whelping. The bitch may seem uneasy, evince signs of pain, be sick, pant a lot, twitch and finally go right off her legs and lie on her side with the legs stiff and her head retracted, panting and frothing at the mouth.

The duration of an attack is variable; it may last some hours, and the bitch is left very exhausted.

It is seldom, if ever, fatal.

Give *Hyoscyamus* 30 half-hourly or less frequently till the convulsion is over.

Feed on a light diet of milk or fish, avoiding red meat for a day or so.

Give *Calc Phos* 6x twice a day until she has ceased feeding her puppies and *China* 3 two-hourly for the possible effects of over lactation for a week.

As a rule, with this treatment, there is no repetition of the convulsions.

PERITONITIS

This is the result of either injury or of chill. The abdomen is hard and painful, and the breathing quickened, and the dog often emits a grunt with each breath. The temperature rises, the dog may vomit or attempt to do so. There is rapid collapse.

It is not uncommon in winter litters where the pup is at the bottom of a heap and is suddenly, by the removal of its brethren, left exposed to a chill.

Aconite 30, three doses at intervals of an hour, in cases arising from a chill may afford relief.

Warm poultices applied to the abdomen are comforting.

Merc Cor. 3 hourly might help when there is much colic, pain, and the abdomen is very swollen — the stool is bloody, slimy and offensive, and the dog keeps straining.

Belladonna 3 hourly (after *Aconite*) if there is sudden, violent invasion.

PERSPIRATION

A dog does not perspire through its skin, but one sometimes meets with cases of puppies in the nest which are unthrifty, and these may become wet with perspiration.

This is a sign of great debility.

See that the dam has good food, plenty of milk and raw meat, and give her *Calc Carb* 6 three times a day if her milk is poor and she is fat and lazy, or *Calc Phos* 6 in the same way if she is thin and poor in condition.

Give the puppies *Calc Phos* 6 or *Calc Carb* 6, whichever is indicated as shown above, three times a day. The remedy can be placed in the mouth quite easily. If they are old enough, give supplementary feeds with a drop of *Haliverol* added.

The puppies may be dusted with powder to dry them off.

They should be kept in an even temperature.

Silica 200, one dose, may alter the whole condition; this must not be repeated in under one week. This is suitable for undersized, weakly pups.

RHEUMATISM

This may affect a dog anywhere, and at most ages, although old dogs are more subject to the complaint.

It may attack the muscles of the neck, when the dog cries out with pain if it tries to move its head, or any of the legs, shoulders or loins.

If the dog has Lumbago badly it may lose the use of its hind legs for a time and become temporarily paralysed.

Keep the dog quiet, in dry quarters, out of draughts.

Give *Rhus Tox* 30 in alternation with *Bryonia* 30, two-hourly until relief is observed, then at longer intervals for a day or two.

Sulphur 30 may be indicated in a dog that suffers from rheumatism in hot weather. Give morning and evening for a few days and repeat when necessary. A dog needing *Sulphur* usually has a lack-lustre coat.

RICKETS

This complaint attacks puppies up to six months old. The joints of the knees and hocks become enlarged, the front legs bowed and the hind legs cow hocked. The bones of the face are also sometimes affected.

The puppy is thin and unthrifty in appearance and in bad cases can hardly walk at all, or walks on the sides of its legs.

The cause of Rickets may be due to improper feeding (possibly of the dam prior to whelping); it may also be due to a lack of sunshine, fresh air, liberty and exercise. Worms may be an additional cause of the trouble. It may be due to calcium deficiency.

If treatment is begun early, the most unlikely cases can be cured completely.

The puppy should be encouraged to walk, be out in the sunshine whenever possible, and be fed on raw meat and milk and eggs only. Cut out all farinaceous food until improvement is shown.

The addition of an *egg* or a teaspoon, according to the size of the puppy, of *Cod Liver Oil* and *Parrish's Syrup Mixture* (4 ozs. of *Cod Liver Oil* mixed with 2 ozs. of *Parrish's Syrup*) and well shaken up, with two meat meals a day, is excellent.

Give *Calc Phos* 6 twice a day in the milk meals (goat's milk is better than cow's) and *Silica* 200 once a week.

Calc Carb 6 or 30 instead of *Calc Phos* 6 may be more suitable to soft, flabby puppies with large heads which appear to be too heavy to support.

See that the puppy is free from worms.

Bonemeal added to the food is very helpful and necessary in cases of rickets.

RINGWORM
Ringworm is caused by a vegetable parasite.

It appears in the form of circular patches of skin which are rough and scaly and there are occasionally some red pimples on the places, the hair appears to be broken off. It is often carried by rats or mice. It is very contagious to other animals and to people.

There are several varieties of the disease, which is often picked up from cows.

Isolate the dog and give it a sulphur bath (2 ozs. of sulphurated potash to 1 gallon of water) once a week.

One dose of *Sulphur* 200 once a week, or *Sulphur* 6 morning and evening.

The kennel, together with all toilet articles, collar, bedding, etc., should be sprayed with 40 per cent *Formaldehyde* solution (do not return the dog to its kennel until the spray has dried).

As a rule three *Sulphur* baths at weekly intervals will effect a cure, unless there has been neglect to disinfect thoroughly.

All suspected contacts should be given a protective bath as well; do not rinse the dog after the bath. Either *Sulphur* or *Chrysarobin Ointment* may be applied to the places between baths (night and morning).

Ringworm is often constitutionally allied to Tuberculosis (which would account for cows being constitutionally liable to Ringworm — it may also account for the immunity to the disease which some people have).

Many cures have been effected by the internal administration of *Bacillinum* 200 once a week or *Sepia* 6, four-hourly, or less often.

External applications to the lesions of *Cod Liver Oil* or *Oil of Lavender* are also useful.

Dogs are, however, not very susceptible to T.B. and the *Sulphur* baths will probably be quite sufficient.

In obstinate cases the internal administration of one of the above-mentioned remedies would expedite a cure.

SHAKING PALSY

Symptoms: Trembling of the limbs, particularly of the back legs, when standing. The dog may walk quite normally and only shake when standing. Old dogs are more often affected than young ones.

Give *Mag Phos* 6 three times a day for a week, then *Kali Phos* 6 in the same way, and continue until an improvement is shown.

Calc Phos 6 may be given intercurrently with the other remedies.

SHOCK

The dog lies on its side in a semi-conscious or unconscious condition; the breathing is slow and the pulse hardly perceptible. The lips and membranes of the eyes are white. The animal is cold and the temperature sub-normal.

This could be the result of internal injury and haemorrhage after an accident, such as being run over by a car, when the case is pretty well hopeless. In shock and collapse from other causes, lay the dog on its right side, with the head low, give *Camphor* 3 every 15-30 minutes, rub the limbs and put hot water bottles round the dog. (Be careful not to burn it.)

Should the shock be known to be the result of an injury, *Arnica* 6 or 30 should be administered internally every two to four hours.

SPRAINS
There is pain and swelling of the injured parts, sometimes heat, followed by lameness.

If the skin is unbroken, bathe the part with *Arnica* lotion (one teaspoonful of ϕ to the pint of water) every three or four hours and give *Arnica* 3 hourly and then at longer intervals as improvement sets in.

When the pain has diminished and the swelling (if any) has subsided, the external applications may be stopped; but continue to give *Arnica* internally three or four times a day.

Keep the dog quiet for a week or two.

Should the sprain be followed later by rheumatic pain and stiffness, give *Rhus Tox* 30 every four hours until relieved; this remedy would be particularly indicated if the dog should be worse at night or worse in cold damp weather and upon first moving from rest.

STINGS

Symptoms: Pain, swelling, and in light coloured dogs, redness of the part stung.

Some dogs will snap at wasps and frequently get stung by them, when the whole head may be greatly swollen.

If possible, remove the sting. Apply a fresh slice of *Onion* to the affected area, this gives speedy relief in bee or wasp stings.

Give *Ledum* 6 every 15 minutes or if there be much swelling, *Apis* 3x every hour until the swelling subsides.

STUTTGART DISEASE

Symptoms: Persistent sickness with fetid breath, furred tongue, ulcers on lips and gums.

Acute cases generally succumb very quickly, though more chronic cases may finally recover after a considerable time.

There may be diarrhoea or dysentery. There may be a rise of temperature, but as a rule the temperature soon falls to sub-normal.

It attacks older dogs rather than young ones, but young dogs are not immune from the disease.

Bathe the ulcers with one in four *T.C.P.* and give *Baptisia* 1x every two hours.

Give honey and water or Slippery Elm food made with milk or plain water if the dog will take it. Avoid all solid food.

Bryonia 30 or *Arsenicum* 30 might be needed to complete the cure when *Baptisia* has cleared away most of the symptoms. One or two doses of either will usually suffice.

When the dog has recovered, give one dose of *Psorinum* 200 to clear up any weakness left after the acute disease.

SUNSTROKE

Symptoms: The dog appears to be suddenly ill and may fall to the ground unconscious. The breathing is heavy, slow and difficult, and the pulse rapid; the membranes of the mouth and the tongue blue and the eyes very congested. There is a high temperature.

The attack is often fatal, or it may be followed by paralysis. The dog may vomit or have diarrhoea.

Beside the direct effect of heat, an attack may be due to the fatigue of physical exertion in great heat. It sometimes occurs some days after exposure to great heat, not necessarily during it.

It is more common in tropical countries than in England.

Camphor inhalations may be given.

Should the dog be conscious and show signs of fear and restlessness, give *Aconite* 6 half-hourly for six doses. If shaky and unsteady when trying to move, give *Gelsemium* 6 every half-hour.

If the animal is unconscious, with tremors and jerking of the limbs and has involuntary evacuations, give *Glonine* 6 frequently at first (every 15 minutes), gradually increasing the intervals.

If the eyes are brilliant and staring with the pupils dilated, *Belladonna* 6 should help, given one-hourly.

Fear and congestion might call for *Cactus* 3, four-hourly, which is valuable for sunstroke and its sequelae.

TEETHING

As a rule the milk teeth of puppies are cut without any trouble at about four weeks old, with slight variations. The second dentition at from four to six months sometimes causes trouble, especially if the puppy has not been sensibly reared and fed and is not free from worms.

It is as well at that time not to over-excite or encourage too violent exercise or the puppy may have convulsions.

Often the permanent teeth come through before the milk teeth have been shed; then the milk teeth should be drawn or the permanent ones may not be straight.

Should the puppy have convulsions, keep it quiet, on a low diet for a few days, substituting fish for meat and avoiding all biscuit meal, and give *Chamomilla* 30 when necessary.

The convulsions will cease once the second teething is completed.

Should the throat be inflamed and the glands, tonsils and fauces swollen and there is stringy saliva, give *Phytolacca* 30 as needed.

THROAT (SORE)
Symptoms: The throat is red and inflamed, there may be an excessive secretion of saliva, and the glands on the outside of the throat may be swollen. The dog is off its food and generally unwell. As this may be a premonitory symptom of Distemper it is wise to isolate the dog and watch for further symptoms (such as a considerable rise of temperature) which will soon declare themselves if that should be the reason.

If the attack is simply due to a chill, keep the dog in, on a light diet, and give *Phytolacca* 30 four-hourly.

TICKS
These parasites are found on dogs in parts of the country where sheep are encountered. They are small, blue or green in colour, with pointed heads which dig into the dog's skin, where they suck the blood and increase in size, and cause considerable irritation.

They should be removed. A drop of *Petrol* or *Turpentine* at the inbedded head will cause them to let go their hold or they may be removed with forceps, taking care not to break them; if broken off and the head left inbedded the place is liable to go septic.

A dab of *Calendula* φ will prevent this.

TONGUE, WARTS ON

Sometimes puppies develop warts on the tongue and mouth. They appear rapidly, singly or in clusters, of greyish colour. The puppy dribbles and has offensive breath and may find difficulty in eating. They are contagious from one puppy to another.

Wash out the mouth several times a day with a lotion made by dissolving a teaspoon of washing soda in half a pint of water. Give *Ferrum Pic* 30 three times a day for a week.

TOOTHACHE

Symptoms: Sometimes, if the dog's teeth are not freed from tartar, the gums recede and suppuration takes place around the tooth and the gums swell and get tender.

It is better to have the bad teeth extracted. Before the extraction give *Arnica* 6 or 30 and continue this for 48 hours after. Bathe the mouth with a solution of *Calendula* (a teaspoon of ϕ in half a pint of warm water). The addition of bonemeal to the dog's food will usually prevent teeth from decaying.

TUMOURS

Symptoms: Growths, causing a swelling of the part of the body affected. It generally forms slowly, which together with a lack of rise of temperature in the early stages distinguishes it from an abscess. Tumours are not, as a rule, painful.

For tumours of the jaws, *Hecla Lava* 6 every four

hours.

Fatty tumours will often disappear with *Calc Carb* 30 given once or twice a day.

For tumours of the breast, give *Phytolacca* 30 twice a day.

If there is a history of many inoculations, give *Thuja* 30 daily for a week and later less frequently.

ULCERS

Symptoms: Open sores on internal or external surface of the body with secretion of pus.

External ulcers should be bathed several times a day with warm *Calendula Lotion* (20 drops of *Calendula* φ to a teacup of water).

Give *Silica* 6 every four hours at first and later *Silica* 30 every two or three days. If the ulcers are very painful, give *Hepar Sulph* 6 and later *Hepar Sulph* 30, instead of *Silica*, in the same way, but *not* together.

VOMITING

In cases of simple vomiting after indigestible food, withhold all food for 24 hours and give *Ipecacuanha* 6 every two hours, which soon checks it.

Dogs often induce vomiting by eating grass, in such cases there is no sense in interfering.

WARTS

These appear on all parts of the body and old dogs are very subject to them.

Give *Thuja* 30 once a day for a week and later at longer intervals. Paint locally with *Thuja* Ø twice a day.

If there be numerous small, itching warts, *Calc Carb* 200 internally once a week.

Ferrum Pic 30 helps to clear up various types of warts. (See Tongue, Warts On.)

WORMS

It is considered that more dogs are killed by worm medicines than by worms themselves.

There are two kinds of worms which trouble dogs.

(1) Round worms (*Ascaris Marginata*). These are similar to common earth-worms, but paler in colour. These are more frequently found in puppies than tapeworm, though occasionally the latter is also found.

A puppy badly infected with worms is unthrifty; the appetite is variable, the stomach is distended, and there may be diarrhoea, vomiting or convulsions.

Worms sometimes pass into the stomach and are vomited.

A puppy's constitution may be so weakened that rickets result, since the worms interfere with the proper assimilation of food.

Well-fed puppies may, however, show very few ill-effects, though they have worms. Some dogs appear to be immune to infection.

The worms' eggs are introduced into the stomach by impure water or food, or by infected soil or from the dam's breasts.

In order to strengthen the constitution of puppies infected with worms it is advisable to give a dose of *Sulphur* 30 if the coat is dry and unthrifty or *Calc Carb* 30 to a fat puppy who seems to be top-heavy yet unthrifty, daily for a week. Do not give *Calc Carb* before *Sulphur*. It follows *Sulphur* well.

Chenopodium 3x and *Cina* 3x twice a day are usually quite effective if continued for a week, discontinued for a week, then repeated persistently, these could be given in alternation.

If there be frequent ineffectual urging to stool and foul breath, give *Spigelia* 30, an occasional dose every two or three days.

In obstinate cases *Nat Phos* 6x will destroy the excess of lactic acid upon which the worms live. A steady course of this remedy is necessary; it may be given two or three times a day for some weeks, or in the 30th potency (*Nat Phos* 30) once or twice a week.

(2) The tapeworm (*Toenia*) is more difficult to expel. The symptoms vary considerably. Some dogs may be infected but show very few symptoms, others lose flesh and suffer from eczema which clears up only when the parasite leaves its host. The bowels are often irregular, the appetite is variable, the coat is dull and unthrifty and the dog has a tucked up appearance. The worm segments, which look like flattened pieces of rice, may be seen moving on the motions at times, or they may be found about the underneath parts of the tail.

Dogs may become infected by eating raw meat or by eating grass which has been infected by sheep or rabbits, or by drinking infected water. Fleas and lice also act as intermediate hosts. Tapeworms do not breed in the dog, but the eggs and larvae pass out of it and are swallowed by some other creature which acts as an intermediate host.

Treatment is as for round worms for the constitutional condition.

Internally, *Filix Mas* φ morning and evening persistently for weeks. In some cases higher potencies such as 30 or 200 in occasional doses are more effective.

When the dog has bloody, slimy and offensive stools, *Merc Cor* 6 morning and evening will sometimes cure Tapeworm.

All worms passed should be burned. The ground should be limed occasionally to prevent re-infection.

WOUNDS

Dogs may be wounded in various ways, by blows, cuts, barbed wire, in fights, etc.

For contused injuries (bruised), give *Arnica* 6, two-hourly at first and then four-hourly. Provided the skin is not broken, apply *Arnica Lotion* (20 drops of φ in about half a cup of water). The bruised parts may be bathed with the lotion, or it may be applied by linen cloths saturated in it and bandaged.

In bruises, contusions, etc., the usual after effects (stiffness, swelling and shock) may be almost entirely prevented by the prompt use of *Arnica* internally.

N.B. *Arnica* should *not* be applied to an open cut, as in some cases it may produce a form of Erysipelas when applied externally in an insufficiently diluted form. It is invaluable for the treatment of bruises and should always be given internally; but where the skin is broken and bleeding, *Calendula* φ may be applied safely externally (or it can be diluted one in ten as it is very effective in this strength); this will do better than any orthodox antiseptic.

In cuts, give *Arnica* 6 two-hourly at first and later four-hourly; externally apply *Calendula* as above.

For punctured wounds as from barbed wire, bites, insect stings, etc., give *Ledum* 6 half-hourly, hourly or two-hourly, according to the severity of the injury. *Ledum* speedily relieves pain and will prevent sepsis, and, if given early enough, will prevent tetanus. Apply *Calendula* externally as indicated above.

For bruised nerves give *Hypericum* 6 two-hourly and apply *Hypericum* φ locally or diluted as above; this will give speedy relief.

For torn and wrenched tendons, synovitis and inflammation of the joints, *Ruta* 6 every two hours.

In fractures, *Symphytum* 6 three times a day until the bone has set.

Calendula Ointment for cuts, septic places, etc., is soothing and produces rapid healing.

Symphytum 6 should be remembered for injuries to the eyes after a blow.

SOME HOMOEOPATHIC CURES

Two Pekes had a battle one week-end. For some reason I was unable to get a veterinary surgeon at once. The smaller dog sustained a leg injury. He was given *Arnica* internally and *Arnica Lotion* was applied to the bad leg. About 48 hours later he was seen by the vet and X-rayed. The X-ray showed the bone to be cracked and the vet hesitated about putting it into a splint, finally deciding against it. The dog was unable to use the leg and I was told it was unlikely that his lameness would ever be cured. The *Arnica* internally was continued and at the end of a week the lameness disappeared completely.

Another disaster with a Pekingese — a very old lady this time with a very bad heart. One day I had left her safely indoors, as she was rather an aggressive old dear, someone else, without my knowledge, let her out. For some unknown reason a quarrel ensued and she was attacked by larger dogs; later I found her lying quite unconscious, cold, in the garden, and at first I thought she was dead. We revived her with *Amyl Nitrate* inhalations and brandy, and with a course of *Crataegus* she completely recovered. Her ear had been badly torn but very rapidly healed up with *Calendula Lotion* externally and *Arnica* internally. Although her heart was very bad she always responded to *Crataegus* or *Spongia* and lived to a venerable old age.

A Cairn Terrier recovering from Hard Pad suffered from diarrhoea which got his owner out of her bed night after night despite veterinary advice and medicines. He was a shivery little dog and hugged the fire. One dose of *Arsenicum* 30 cleared up the trouble.

During a virulent outbreak of Hard Pad, a Basenji dog, hitherto unaffected, one morning came out of his kennel looking miserable and cold, he had pinky diarrhoea. He was given one dose of *Arsenicum* 200 and that cleared all the symptoms.

His brother who had been in actual contact with

some affected puppies was given *Distemperinum* 30 as a preventative and escaped the contagion altogether. The breed had not, at that time, been established in England long enough to have got much immunity to the complaint, which they took very badly.

A Siamese kitten in the last stages of Cat Flu was given one dose of *Pyrogen* 30 and made a miraculous recovery.

Another Siamese kitten had a virulent attack of Cat Flu. Its mouth was ulcerated and smelt abominably. *Baptisia* cured her.

A young cat had a deep cut on its eye. How it had happened, whether in a fight or whether it ran into something, we did not know. It was right on the pupil. *Arnica* internally and *Calendula Lotion* externally cured it completely without leaving a scar.

A relation's cat went wrong having kittens, which had to be removed by a Caesarian operation and she was spayed at the same time. She was returned home to her owners running a temperature and ordered to be given M. & B. tablets. The owners preferred Homoeopathic treatment and bathed the scar with *Calendula Lotion* and administered *Pyrogen.* The cat made an excellent recovery, to the surprise of the vet, who expected her to die.

A Basenji puppy, literally lacking 'vital heat', miserable, chilly and stationary in growth. One dose of *Silica* 200 altered the whole picture.

An Alsatian dog, subject to eczema, was in my care during many of the war years, his owner was astonished at the dog's freedom from his constitutional complaint, having spent a small fortune on orthodox cures. *Sulphur* in high potency was the only remedy used.

One evening a young Golden Labrador puppy (two days after a sudden violent attack of Hysteria after tearing about on a very hot day) vomited and passed a lot of blood and collapsed. One dose of *Phosphorus* was administered; some hours later as the dog was dribbling a lot she was given one dose of *Nat Mur.* The next morning she was apparently perfectly well and there was no repetition of the attack. No further medication was needed. Soon after she went into training and she did well at work.

A Poodle with chronic catarrh of the middle ear, a dog with a very sensitive back had been under orthodox treatment for months with no improvement in the condition, was cured by a few doses of *Tellurium.*

INDEX

INDEX

INDEX